This book is to be returned on or before
the last date stamped below. S-7√

BOOK No. 22188214S CLASS No. ....

GRAPHIC EXPEDITIONS

EXPLORING TITANIC

AN *Isabel Soto*
HISTORY ADVENTURE

Agnieszka Biskup

illustrated by Al Bigley and Bill Anderson

www.raintreepublishers.co.uk
Visit our website to find out
more information about
Raintree books.

Phone 0845 6044371
Fax +44 (0) 1865 312263
Email myorders@capstonepub.co.uk

Customers from outside the UK please telephone +44 1865 312262

Raintree is an imprint of Capstone Global Library Limited, a company incorporated in England and
Wales having its registered office at 7 Pilgrim Street, London EC4V 6LB
Registered company number: 6695882

"Raintree" is a registered trademark of Pearson Education Limited, under licence to Capstone Global
Library Limited

Text © Capstone Press 2010
First published by Capstone Press in 2010
First published in hardback in the United Kingdom by Capstone Global Library in 2010
First published in paperback in the United Kingdom by Capstone Global Library in 2011
The moral rights of the proprietor have been asserted.

British Library Cataloguing in Publication Data
Biskup, Agnieszka – Exploring Titanic: an Isabel Soto history adventure
A full catalogue record for this book is available from the British Library.

ISBN 978 1 406 21442 0 (hardback)
14 13 12 11 10
10 9 8 7 6 5 4 3 2 1

Art Director and Designer: Alison Thiele
Cover Artist: Tod Smith
Colourist: Michael Kelleher
UK Editor: Diyan Leake
UK Production: Victoria Fitzgerald
Originated by Capstone Global Library
Printed and bound in China by South China Printing Company Limited

Photo Credits: AP Images p. 25 (Nauticus); Getty Images Inc. p . 17 (Hulton Archive);
Shutterstock p. 19 (Jurgen Ziewe)

Design Elements: Shutterstock/Chen Ping Hung (framed edge design); mmmm (world
map design); Mushakesa (abstract lines design); Najin (old parchment design)

CONTENTS

The International History Museum, present day

Thanks for coming so quickly, Izzy. We need your help for our new exhibit. Come to my office, and I'll explain.

FLAP FLAP FLAP FLAP

Lead the way.

INTERNATIONAL HISTORY MUSEUM

The new exhibit is about the *Titanic*. I'm sure you know about it?

Of course! It's one of the most famous ships of all time. It sank on its very first voyage.

6

It's one of the worst peacetime sea disasters ever. More than 1,500 people died when *Titanic* sank on 15 April 1912.
That's correct. We'd like you to learn more about why the *Titanic* sank.
We know the ship hit an iceberg. But what made the accident so deadly?
To understand what happened, I'll first need to learn about ocean voyages up to that time.
I'll start by going back to early 1912.
Remember, Izzy, you can't try to change the past.
I know. If I did, who knows how it might change the present? Wish me luck!

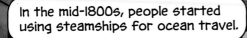

In the mid-1800s, people started using steamships for ocean travel.

Steamships were larger and faster than the old sailing ships. People could travel across the Atlantic Ocean in about two weeks.

Today's ships carry thousands of immigrants to America for the chance of a better life.

Have you heard of the *Titanic*?

Who hasn't? Some people say she's like a floating palace. You should go see her before she sets sail.

I will. Thank you for your time.

Titanic has four funnels. Each one is big enough to drive two trains through. The first three funnels are chimneys for the coal furnaces. The fourth funnel brings fresh air into the engine rooms.

She can cruise at a speed of about 21 knots. That's about 39 kilometres, or 24 miles, per hour.

I notice there are only 20 lifeboats. That isn't enough room for all the people onboard, is it?

No, but don't worry. We actually have four more lifeboats than the law requires. Now let me show you how beautiful *Titanic* is on the inside.

First-class staterooms are large and have the finest furnishings. Some even have a private bathroom.

Second-class passengers enjoy rooms that are superior to most first-class cabins on other ships.

Our third-class cabins are small. But they're clean and comfortable.

We even have two Marconi wireless sets onboard. Passengers can have their messages sent while we're still at sea.

In an emergency, we could use the wireless to call for help. But I'm certain that won't be necessary.

Thanks for the tour. She's a beautiful ship.

RESCUE AT SEA

Just after midnight on 15 April 1912, RMS *Carpathia* received a distress call from *Titanic*. The *Carpathia* was more than 80 kilometres (50 miles) away. Captain Arthur Rostron raced his ship through dangerous ice fields to get to the *Titanic*. But *Carpathia* couldn't reach *Titanic* before it sank. At about 4.00 the following morning, *Carpathia's* crew picked up 705 *Titanic* survivors. Rostron and his crew were considered heroes because of their quick response to the disaster.

But at 11.40 in the evening, lookout man Frederick Fleet spotted an iceberg right ahead of the ship. Orders were given to turn the ship, but it was too late. The ship's right side grazed the iceberg. A few minutes later, *Titanic* came to a dead stop.

SCREEEEEECH!

DEADLY ICE

Only about 10 percent of an iceberg is visible above water. Below the water's surface, an iceberg's sharp edges can puncture a ship's hull.

There was no obvious damage on the upper decks. Passengers even played with some of the ice.

But below the waterline, the iceberg pierced the ship's hull. The ship's chief designer, Thomas Andrews, inspected the damage.

VVROOOSSH!

This looks bad!

I'm afraid we have only an hour or two before the ship sinks.

Captain Smith ordered the wireless operators to call for help. By midnight, the ship's officers started lowering lifeboats.

But there weren't enough lifeboats for everyone.

At first, people didn't think the situation was very serious. The first lifeboats weren't even half full when they were lowered.

But things soon became chaotic. Distress flares were sent up to alert ships in the area. The ship's band played music to help keep people calm. Those brave men kept playing until the ship went down.

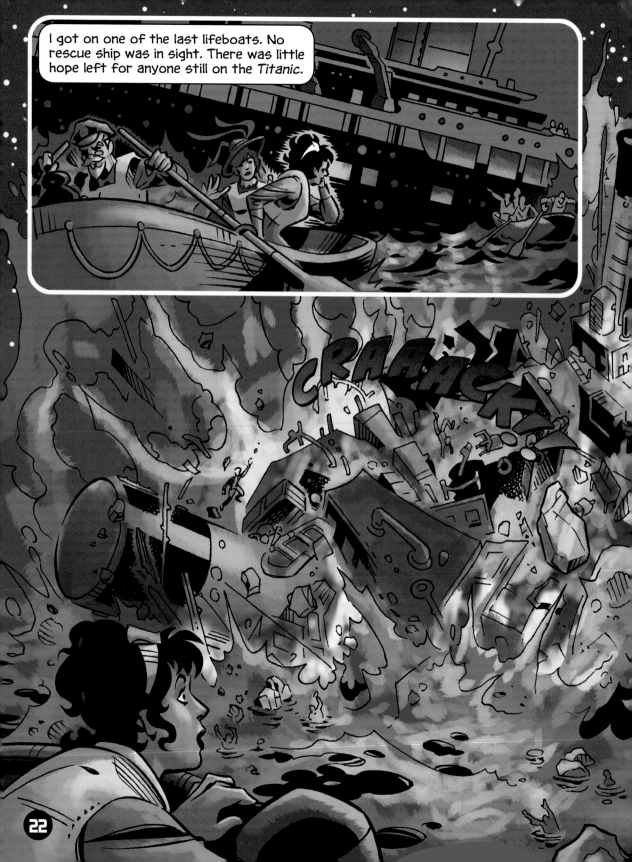

I got on one of the last lifeboats. No rescue ship was in sight. There was little hope left for anyone still on the *Titanic*.

CRAAACK

As the ship's bow sank deeper, her stern rose up. Then I heard a sound like an explosion. *Titanic* broke in half! The ship finally sank at 2.20 in the morning.

BA-DOOOM!!

I think Captain Smith and Mr Andrews went down with the ship. Most of my fellow crew members are missing.

I've heard that many of the third-class passengers are missing too. People can't survive for long in these icy waters.

I'm so sorry. Thank you both for talking to me.

About 600 kilometres (370 miles) off the coast of Newfoundland, Canada, present day

Titanic's final resting place was unknown for more than 70 years.

The ship was finally found in 1985 by oceanographers Robert Ballard and Jean-Louis Michel.

The wreck lies more than 3 kilometres, or 2 miles, deep.

Have scientists learned any new information about how *Titanic* sank?

It was once thought that the iceberg cut one huge gash in the side of the ship.

But sonar images showed six narrow openings in the hull. Six of *Titanic's* watertight compartments flooded. She sank quickly after that. We have some rivet samples in our lab. Let's go back up, and I'll show you.

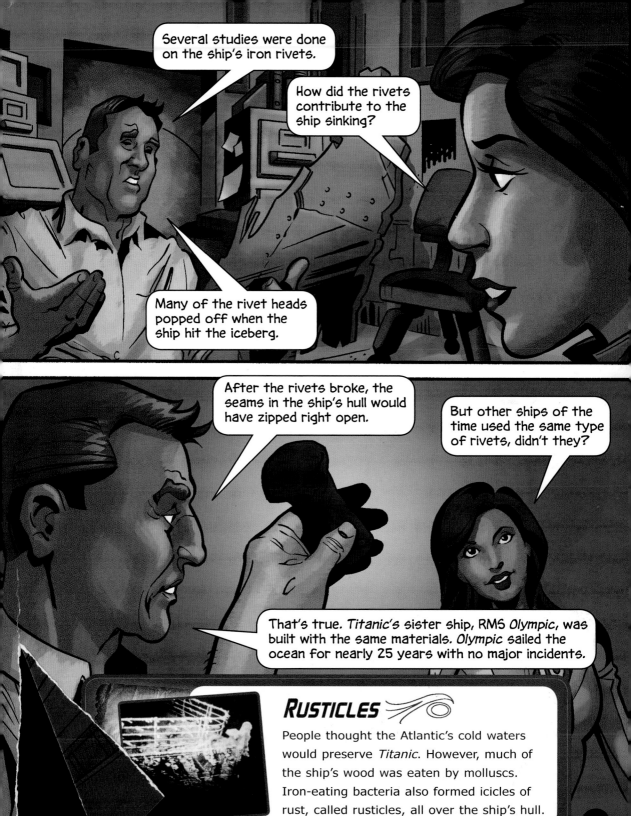

Several studies were done on the ship's iron rivets.

How did the rivets contribute to the ship sinking?

Many of the rivet heads popped off when the ship hit the iceberg.

After the rivets broke, the seams in the ship's hull would have zipped right open.

But other ships of the time used the same type of rivets, didn't they?

That's true. *Titanic's* sister ship, RMS *Olympic*, was built with the same materials. *Olympic* sailed the ocean for nearly 25 years with no major incidents.

RUSTICLES

People thought the Atlantic's cold waters would preserve *Titanic*. However, much of the ship's wood was eaten by molluscs. Iron-eating bacteria also formed icicles of rust, called rusticles, all over the ship's hull.

Waves that hit an iceberg help show its position, especially at night. When the sea is calm, icebergs are very difficult to spot in the dark.

 The lifeboats on *Titanic* only had room for 1,178 people. Many of the first lifeboats were lowered only partially filled. If the lifeboats had been completely filled, almost 500 more people could have been saved.

MORE ABOUT

NAME: Isabel "Izzy" Soto
INTERESTS: People and places
BUILD: Athletic   *HAIR:* Dark Brown
EYES: Brown   *HEIGHT:* 1.70 m

WISP: The Worldwide Inter-dimensional Space/Time Portal developed by Max Axiom at Axiom Laboratory.

BACKSTORY: Isabel "Izzy" Soto caught the humanities bug as a little girl. Every night, her grandfather told her about his adventures exploring ancient ruins in South America. He believed people can learn a lot from other cultures and places.

Izzy's interest in cultures followed her through school and beyond. She studied history and geography. On one research trip, she discovered an ancient stone with mysterious energy. Izzy took the stone to Super Scientist Max Axiom, who determined that the stone's energy cuts across space and time. Harnessing the power of the stone, he built a device called the WISP. It opens windows to any place and any time. Although she must not use the WISP to change history, Izzy now explores events wherever and whenever they happen, solving a few mysteries along the way.

GLOSSARY

bow front end of a ship

compartment section inside a ship that is divided by watertight walls and doors

exhibit display that shows something to the public

flare burst of light shot from a gun to announce a person's presence or position

funnel smokestack on a steamship

hull main body of a ship

iceberg huge piece of ice that floats in the ocean. Icebergs break off from glaciers.

immigrant someone who comes from one country to live permanently in another country

oceanographer scientist who studies the ocean and ocean life

rivet strong metal bolt that is used to fasten something together

RMS short for "Royal Mail Ship". The letters RMS appear before the names of ships that carry mail under contract by Royal Mail.

sonar a device that uses sound waves to find underwater objects; sonar stands for sound navigation and ranging.

SOS signal sent out by a ship or a plane to call for urgent help

stern back end of a ship

wireless device that uses radio waves to send telegraph messages

FIND OUT MORE

Books

Titanic: An Edwardian Girl's Diary, 1912, Ellen Emerson White (Scholastic, 2008)

The Titanic, 1912, Vic Parker (Heinemann Library, 2006)

Titanic Tragedy, Vincent McDonnell (Collins, 2007)

Titanic, Martin Jenkins and Brian Sanders (Walker, 2007)

Internet sites

http://www.britannica.com/titanic/
Click on "Start" on this Encyclopedia Britannica website and then on "Enter the Exhibit" to view a gallery of pictures of the *Titanic*, from the building of the ship, to people and things on board during her first and only voyage, and discovery of the wreckage.

http://adventure.howstuffworks.com/titanic.htm
This website has a photo gallery, information, and a video about the *Titanic*.

http://magma.nationalgeographic.com/ngexplorer/0411/articles/mainarticle.html
This page from the National Geographic website has photos and an article on the sinking of the *Titanic* in 1912 and of the discovery of the wreckage in 1984.